The Essential
Parents'
Guide
to Primary
MATHS

❖

Strategies for solving challenging Maths Problems

Dr Fong Ho Kheong
PhD, University of London

FEDERAL
PUBLICATIONS

Times Media Private Limited
A member of the Times Publishing Group
Times Centre, 1 New Industrial Road, Singapore 536196
E-mail: fps@tpl.com.sg
Online Book Store: http://www.timesone.com.sg/fpl

First published 2002
Reprinted 2002, 2003

ISBN 981-01-7458-6

Designed by: Kent Ng

Printed by B & Jo Enterprise Pte Ltd, Singapore

Preface

The Essential Parents' Guide to Primary Maths: Strategies for Solving Challenging Maths Problems is written primarily for parents. Currently, the new focus in mathematics education is on solving mathematical problems. Parents can use this guide to learn and master various strategies to help their children solve challenging and non-routine mathematical problems encountered at the upper primary level.

This guide consists of three parts:

Part A focuses on the application of the various **problem-solving heuristics**. These are especially useful for solving non-routine problems.

Part B focuses on the application of the **Model Approach** and relevant concepts required to solve mathematical problems. The Model Approach is dealt with in greater detail because it is applicable in many mathematical topics covered at the primary level.

Part C focuses on the application of strategies to solve **challenging examination problems** especially to prepare children taking the PSLE.

Worked examples are given for each strategy so that parents can learn to apply these strategies. Parents are encouraged to attempt the problems in 'Let's Apply' with their children.

I hope that through constant practice in solving mathematical problems, your child can develop his or her creativity further, become more flexible in thinking and skilful at solving some of the practical problems encountered.

Dr Fong Ho Kheong
PhD, University of London

Contents

Part

The Heuristic Approach

There are two types of mathematical problems, routine and non-routine ones. Routine problems can be easily solved by applying the 4 operations which are addition, subtraction, multiplication and division. However, to solve challenging problems and non-routine ones, you require the four operations and special strategies.

The task of solving challenging and non-routine problems is made less arduous when you know the correct strategies to use. It is therefore beneficial for you as parents to learn and master as many different strategies as possible. In doing so, you will be able to help your child solve a variety of problems.

Part A of this book deals with 7 strategies. You can go through the worked examples and learn how to apply the strategies. Then you can attempt to do the questions provided with your child.

The 7 strategies are:
- Guess and Check
- Use Pattern
- Use Lateral Thinking
- Use Deductive Thinking
- Use Modelling Approach
- Use Investigation
- Use Set Concept

Through constant practice, your child can gain confidence and become more creative in his approach to solving problems.

1   Guess And Check

The 'Guess And Check' strategy is a powerful one that uses guessing and checking in the process of solving mathematical problems. To apply this strategy, you need to understand the problem first. Next, you have to note the conditions given in the problem which have to be satisfied. Finally, when you make a guess, you have to check if the guessed answer fulfils all the required conditions. If one or more of the conditions are not satisfied, then the answer is incorrect.

What To Do

Step 1: Guess the answer.
To make an intelligent guess, your children can start off with numbers somewhere around the middle of a given number in the question. Then they can decide to increase or decrease the numbers for their next guess.

Step 2: Check if your guess is correct.
Make use of relevant information to check your guess. All the conditions in the problem must be satisfied.

Example 1

Uncle Joe has some rabbits and chickens on his farm. There are 12 animals and 40 legs altogether. How many of each animal does Uncle Joe have?

Solution

Identify the conditions in the problem:
1. There are 12 animals.
2. There are 40 legs.

Make a guess

6 rabbits, 6 chickens

Notice that we start off with 6 as it is the middle number between 1 and 12.

Check your guess

We assume each rabbit has 4 legs, each chicken has 2 legs.

6 rabbits + 6 chickens = 12 animals (*satisfies 1st condition*)

Animal	Number of legs
Rabbit	$6 \times 4 = 24$
Chicken	$6 \times 2 = 12$

Total number of legs is 24 + 12 = 36. (*does not satisfy 2nd condition*)

Conclusion   Wrong guess!

Make another guess

8 rabbits, 4 chickens

Check your guess

8 rabbits + 4 chickens = 12 animals (*satisfies 1st condition*)

Animal	Number of legs
Rabbit	$8 \times 4 = 32$
Chicken	$4 \times 2 = 8$

Total number of legs is 32 + 8 = 40. (*satisfies 2nd condition*)

Conclusion   Right guess! That's the answer.

Note: This guess and check procedure is a form of mathematical thinking. If we start off with some correct assumptions, they will lead to valid conclusions.

Example 2

Wendy went to a bakery to buy cakes and doughnuts. She spent $14 altogether on 30 cakes and doughnuts. Each cake cost 40¢ and each doughnut cost 50¢. How many of each did she buy?

Solution

Identify the conditions in the problem:
1. Wendy bought 30 cakes and doughnuts.
2. She spent $14.

Make a guess

> 15 cakes, 15 doughnuts
>
> Notice that we start off with 15 as it is the middle number between 1 and 30.

Check your guess

> 15 cakes + 15 doughnuts = 30 cakes and doughnuts
>
> (satisfies 1st condition)

Cost of cakes	Cost of doughnuts
15 × 40¢ = $6.00	15 × 50¢ = $7.50

$6.00 + $7.50 = $13.50 (*does not satisfy 2nd condition*)

Conclusion   Wrong guess!

Make another guess

> 10 cakes, 20 doughnuts

Check your guess

> 10 cakes + 20 doughnuts = 30 cakes and doughnuts
>
> (satisfies 1st condition)

Cost of cakes	Cost of doughnuts
10 × 40¢ = $4.00	20 × 50¢ = $10.00

$4.00 + $10.00 = $14.00 (*satisfies 2nd condition*)

Conclusion   Right guess! That's the answer.

Let's Apply

1. In a car park, there are 14 cars and motorcycles. Altogether, 44 wheels are counted. How many of each type of vehicle are there?

2. Muthu owns a pet shop. He has 18 parrots and hamsters altogether. The pets have 58 legs in total. How many of each type of pet does Muthu have?

3. It costs 10¢ to mail a postcard and 15¢ for a letter. Brenda wrote to 12 friends and spent $1.55 on postage. How many postcards and how many letters did she write?

4. Peter and John began playing noughts and crosses. Before they began, each had the same number of rubber bands. Each time Peter won a round, John gave him 5 rubber bands. Each time John won a round, Peter gave him 3 rubber bands.

   After playing 16 rounds, Peter and John had the same number of rubber bands each. How many rounds of the game did each win?

2 Use Pattern

The 'Use Pattern' Strategy can be applied to solve a mathematical problem if a pattern can be detected when a set of data is collected and/or manipulated. You can then make use of the pattern to solve the problem or generalise a solution.

What to Do

> **Step 1:** List the data and look for a pattern.
>
> **Step 2:** Use the pattern to form a conjecture or hypothesis (assumption) and solve the problem.

Example 1

Find the total number of squares on a 4 × 4 checkerboard.

Solution

Here is a 4 × 4 checkerboard.

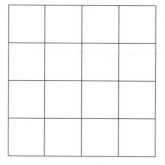

You can solve the problem by counting the possible number of squares on the checkerboard. However, this method is not systematic and you may actually miss out on counting some squares or counting them twice. A more systematic method is to find out how many types of squares there are in the checkerboard and count them.

If you look at the 4×4 checkerboard carefully, you can identify 4 types of squares as shown.

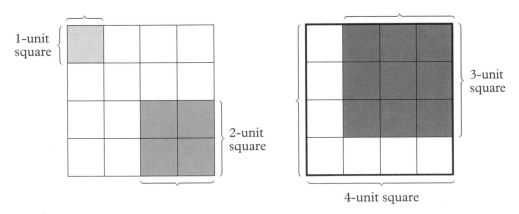

The table below shows the number of squares for each type.

Type of square	Number of squares
1-unit square	$4 \times 4 = 4^2 = 16$
2-unit square	$3 \times 3 = 3^2 = 9$
3-unit square	$2 \times 2 = 2^2 = 4$
4-unit square	$1 \times 1 = 1^2 = 1$

From the table, you can count the number of squares on a 4×4 checkerboard. There are $(16 + 9 + 4 + 1)$ or 30 squares altogether.

When you examine the solution, you will notice that the number of squares for each type is a **square number**. These square numbers, '4^2, 3^2, 2^2 and 1^2', form a pattern.

Is it possible to solve other similar problems based on this observation? Can you generalise a solution for such problems?

Let's consider another similar problem and examine its solution.

Example 2

Find the total number of squares on a 6 × 6 checkerboard.

Solution

Here is a 6 × 6 checkerboard.

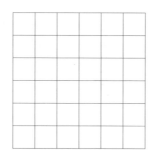

You can identify 6 types of squares on a 6 × 6 checkerboard. The table below shows the number of squares for each type.

Type of square	Number of squares
1-unit square	$6 \times 6 = 6^2 = 36$
2-unit square	$5 \times 5 = 5^2 = 25$
3-unit square	$4 \times 4 = 4^2 = 16$
4-unit square	$3 \times 3 = 3^2 = 9$
5-unit square	$2 \times 2 = 2^2 = 4$
6-unit square	$1 \times 1 = 1^2 = 1$

$$\text{Total number of squares} = 36 + 25 + 16 + 9 + 4 + 1$$
$$= 91$$

There are 91 squares on a 6 × 6 checkerboard. You will notice that there is a similar pattern of numbers as in Example 1. That is, the number of squares for each type is actually a square number. This pattern of numbers can be used to solve similar mathematical problems.

Note: From the two examples, you will realise that when you have a 4 × 4 checkerboard (or grid) and a 6 × 6 checkerboard (or grid), you begin with 4^2 and 6^2 respectively as shown in the tables.

Therefore, you may generalise that if you are given an $n \times n$ checkerboard (or grid), you begin with n^2 and work out your answer accordingly.

Let's Apply

1. Find the total number of squares on an 8 × 8 checkerboard.

2. Find the total number of squares on a 12 × 12 checkerboard.

3. Dots are used to form triangles as shown below. 3, 6 and 9 are examples of triangle dot numbers.

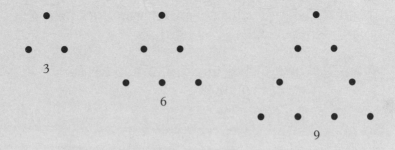

(a) What triangle dot number has 10 dots on a side? Derive a pattern for this.

(b) What triangle dot number has 25 dots on a side? Use the pattern derived in part **(a)** to find the answer.

4. Dots are used to form pentagons as shown below. 5, 10 and 15 are examples of pentagon dot numbers.

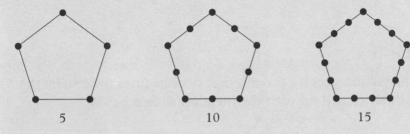

(a) How many dots are there on each side of the dot figure for pentagon dot number 35?

(b) How many dots are there on each side of the dot figure for pentagon dot number 195?

3 Use Lateral Thinking

The 'Use Lateral Thinking' strategy is required when you cannot solve the mathematical problems by using logic or other conventional ways of thinking. Instead, you have to use your imagination to think of solutions which are not obvious at first.

What To Do

Step 1: Ask yourself as many relevant questions as possible.

Step 2: Think divergently to come up with any possible solution.

Example 1

The diagram below shows 5 dots. Draw 3 straight lines to connect the 5 dots without lifting your pencil from the diagram.

Solution

If you think convergently and attempt to draw lines to connect the 5 dots, you are likely to end up with the diagram shown below.

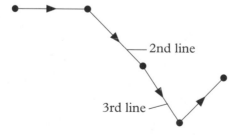

In this solution, you have used 4 lines to connect the 5 dots. Thus, you have to ask yourself how you can reduce from using 4 lines to 3 lines in your solution. To achieve this, you will have to think of how you can use 1 line instead of 2 lines to connect some of the points.

Notice from the diagram below how the 2nd line and 3rd line from the previous diagram are straightened into 1 line. Thus you have reduced the number of lines used from 4 to 3. Note that the turning point between the second dot and third dot is outside the dots. Therefore, to solve this mathematical problem, one of the turning points has to be outside any of the 5 given dots.

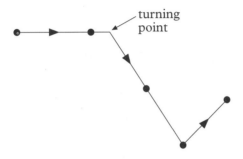

The diagram below shows another possible solution.

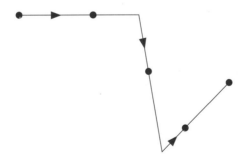

Note that two of the turning points are outside the dots.

Example 2

Divide a circular cake into 8 equal parts using only 3 cuts.

Solution

Normally, you cut a cake from the top. However, for this mathematical problem, if you cut the cake in this way, you will need 4 cuts to get 8 equal parts as shown below.

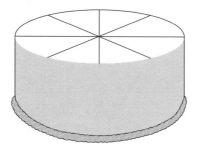

Thus, to solve this problem, you need to think divergently and cut the cake twice from the top and once across from the side of the cake to get 8 equal parts with 3 cuts only.

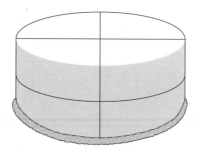

Note: From examples 1 and 2, you will realise that you need to use lateral thinking to solve problems when new ideas are required.

Let's Apply

1. The diagram below shows 9 dots arranged in 3 rows and 3 columns. Draw 4 straight lines to connect the 9 points without lifting your pencil from the diagram.

2. Twelve matchsticks are arranged to form 4 equal squares as shown below. Which 2 matchsticks should you remove so that only 2 squares are left?

3. You can form a triangle using 3 matchsticks as shown below. How do you form 4 such triangles with 6 matchsticks?

4. Amy stands on the right-hand side of Brenda. Carol stands on the right-hand side of Amy. Show their positions given that Brenda stands on the right-hand side of Carol.

4 Use Deductive Thinking

The 'Use Deductive Thinking' strategy can be used to solve mathematical problems that involve logic. To solve such problems, you are required to think logically and draw conclusions from the information given. You can usually solve a problem faster by making deduction rather than by guessing the answer.

What To Do

Step 1: Associate and relate the information given to generate further information.

Step 2: Make use of all the given relevant information. Reason in a logical way. Draw conclusions correctly or eliminate possibilities to arrive at the correct answer.

Example 1

In the diagram below, fill in the circles using the numbers 2, 3, 4, 5, 6 and 7. The numbers on each side of the triangle must add up to 12.

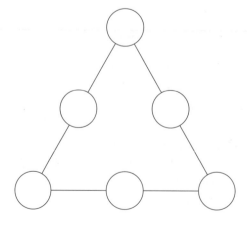

Solution

In this question, you can make use of the following information to help you solve the problem:
(i) a set of given numbers
(ii) the numbers in the circles on each side of the triangle must add up to 12

Firstly, using the given numbers, find sets of numbers that add up to 12. You have to use all the numbers and each number can only be used once to fill the circles.

Secondly, note the different positions of the circles. The numbers to be placed in the circles are related to the positions of the circles.

Thirdly, deduce logically that a number to be placed in the corner circle can be used to form two combinations of numbers. Likewise, you can also deduce that a number to be placed in the centre circle can only be used to form one combination of numbers.

Fourthly, decide which numbers to fill in the circles. To do this, you can list the sets of numbers that add up to 12 as follows:

$$\boxed{2} + 7 + \boxed{3} = 12, \qquad \boxed{2} + 6 + \boxed{4} = 12, \qquad \boxed{3} + \boxed{4} + 5 = 12$$

From the above combinations of numbers, you will notice that **2, 3** and **4** appear twice whereas 5, 6 and 7 appear only once. You can then deduce that 2, 3 and 4 can be placed in the corner circles and 5, 6 and 7 are to be placed in the centre circles of the sides of the triangle as shown.

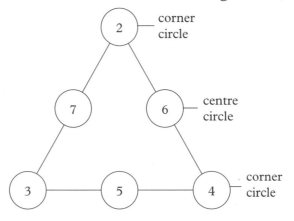

Note: You need to consider how numbers are related to get 12 and the positions of the circles so that you can fill in the numbers correctly.

Example 2

In the inequality 73 > 65 + _____ , what is the greatest possible number and the smallest possible number in the blank?

Note: '>' means 'greater than'.

Solution

In this problem, assume that you are working on whole numbers including zero. Since it is an inequality, 73 is greater than 72, where 72 is the greatest number you can place on the right-hand side. Therefore, the answer in the blank is 7 because (65 + 7) equals 72. The smallest possible number in the blank is zero.

Note: In examples 1 and 2, you have learnt how to use deductive thinking to get the answers. This approach is useful in solving classic magic-square problems.

Let's Apply

1. In the diagram below, fill in the circles using the numbers 1, 2, 3, 4, 5 and 6. The numbers on each side of the triangle must add up to 10.

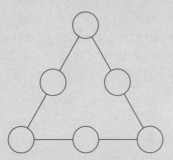

2. Fill in the numbers 2, 3, 6 and 8 in the boxes below. Use each number only once.

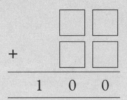

3. In the inequality 146 > 127 + _____, what is the greatest possible whole number and the smallest possible whole number in the blank?

4. In the diagram below, fill in the boxes using all the numbers from 1 to 9 inclusive. The sum of the numbers which are arranged horizontally, vertically and diagonally must be 15.

    (**Hint:** There are 4 corner boxes, 4 centre boxes at the sides and 1 centre box in the middle of the square.)

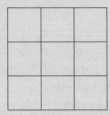

5 Use Modelling Approach

The 'Use Modelling Approach' is a strategy used to solve mathematical problems by looking at them from different perspectives. In other words, you can first treat the same problem using a different situation and then relate the new situation to the original problem. There is no fixed rule as to what new objects or situations you need to use to model after the problem. You can try applying this strategy when you cannot solve your problem by using other strategies.

What to Do

Step 1: Think carefully of a new situation to model after the problem.

Step 2: Translate the new situation to the original problem and solve it.

Example 1

The diagram below shows the arrangement of 5 identical circles. Draw a straight line to divide the 5 circles into 2 equal parts.

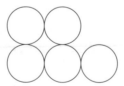

Solution

It is not easy to solve this problem simply by examining the 5 identical circles. You have to look at the problem from a different perspective. For example, you can first consider the circles as rectangles or squares. It is easier to solve a problem that involves rectangles or squares. Next, you have to find out the underlying principles of dividing rectangles or squares into 2 equal parts.

You can start off by considering the possible straight lines that can be drawn to divide a rectangle into 2 equal parts. Many of you might think that there are only 4 ways to do so as shown below.

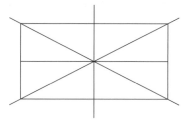

However, if you are more creative, you will be able to draw another line to divide the rectangle into 2 equal parts as shown below.

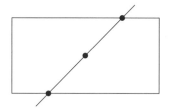

In fact, you can divide the rectangle into 2 equal parts in infinite number of ways. Notice that as long as a line is drawn through the centre of the rectangle, it divides it into 2 equal parts. This underlying principle is also applicable to circles. Now, using the same principle, divide the compound figure (formed by using a square and a rectangle) shown below into 2 equal parts.

You can draw the line as shown. It passes through the centres of the 2 shapes.

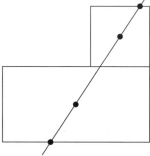

Having considered the situation of a square and a rectangle, you can now apply the same principle to divide the 5 identical circles. Firstly, treat the 5 circles as a compound figure. Secondly, draw a line to divide it. The diagrams below show 4 ways you can do this.

(i)

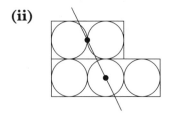

(ii)

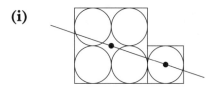

(iii)

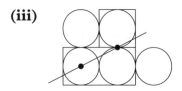

(iv)

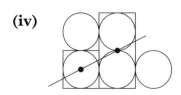

Note: You can solve the problem easily by looking at it from a different perspective.

Example 2

How do you make use of a 5-litre bucket and a 3-litre bucket to measure 4 litres of water?

Solution

The problem may be solved by filling and pouring from one bucket into another a few times and juggling the amount of water in the buckets until you get 4 litres. However, this method is tedious and time-consuming.

Alternatively, you can solve the problem by using the modelling approach. Consider the problem from a different perspective. Treat it as one of manipulating numbers instead.

To begin with, ask yourself how you can manipulate the numbers 3 and 5 to get 4. There are many ways to do this. For example, $(2 \times 3 - 5) + 3 = 4$.

Next, translate this mathematical statement into action by pouring water from one bucket into another. The number 2 in the mathematical statement means that you have to fill the 3-litre bucket with water twice. You will end up with 6 litres of water. Therefore, to measure 4 litres of water, you will have to pour water from the 3-litre bucket into the 5-litre bucket twice. You will then have 1 litre of water left over. Now empty the 5-litre bucket and transfer the 1 litre of water into the 5-litre bucket. Fill up the 3-litre bucket again and add the water to the 1 litre of water in the 5-litre bucket. Finally, you will have 4 litres of water.

Note: You have translated a situation of numbers into one of measuring 4 litres of water to solve the problem.

Let's Apply

1. Draw a straight line to divide the following circles into 2 equal parts.

   (a)

   (b)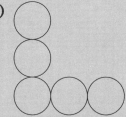

2. You are given a 3-litre bucket and a 5-litre bucket. How do you use them to measure
   (a) 1 litre of water,
   (b) 6 litres of water,
   (c) 7 litres of water?
   (You may assume that you have a big bucket which can hold about 10 litres of water.)

3. You are given 2 oranges. How do you make 3 equal glasses of orange juice for your friends?
   (You are not allowed to use a graduated measuring cylinder.)

4. How do you measure half a glass of wine if the glass is conical in shape?
   (You are not allowed to use a graduated measuring cylinder.)

6 Use Investigation

In the 'Use Investigation' strategy, you apply a standard mathematical thinking investigation to solve mathematical problems. This typical approach involves a sequence of mathematical processes such as collecting data, looking for pattern, making hypothesis, testing the hypothesis and making generalisation. Usually, most problem solvers will omit some of the steps and apply the hypothesis directly to come up with a solution.

What to Do

Step 1: Collect a set of data from the information given. Look for a pattern from the data.

Step 2: Form a hypothesis based on the patterns. Test the validity of the hypothesis.

Step 3: Generalise the solution when you have tested a few cases and found the hypothesis to be valid in all cases.

Example

Find the 304th odd number of the sequence of numbers 1, 2, 3, 4, ...

Solution

Data collection

You can collect a set of data by finding the first few odd numbers. Then from this set of odd numbers, you have to look for a pattern. If you cannot detect any pattern, then you have to transform it into a form that will give you a pattern. The procedure to do this is shown below.

> The 1st odd number = 1 = $1 + 0$
> The 2nd odd number = 3 = $2 + 1$
> The 3rd odd number = 5 = $3 + 2$
> The 4th odd number = 7 = $4 + 3$, and so on.

From the sequence of odd numbers 1, 3, 5, 7, ..., you can predict that the 5th odd number is 9. You can find the 304th odd number if you carry on from here. However, this method is tedious and time-consuming.

Looking For Patterns

If you look at the last column of numbers above, you will notice that the odd numbers have been transformed into a new set of numbers using the addition operation. That is,

> $1 = 1 + 0$,   (1st addend is 1, 2nd addend is 0)
> $3 = 2 + 1$,   (1st addend is 2, 2nd addend is 1)
> $5 = 3 + 2$,   (1st addend is 3, 2nd addend is 2)
> $7 = 4 + 3$ ....   (1st addend is 4, 2nd addend is 3)

What patterns can you observe from this sequence of addition numbers?

You will notice that in each set of addition numbers,

(i) the second addend is one less than the first addend,
(ii) the numerical value of the first addend is the same as the nth odd number. For example, the 4th odd number is 7 and $4 + 3 = 7$.

These two patterns apply to other odd numbers in the sequence too.

Forming A Hypothesis

Once you have noticed the two patterns, you can figure out how to solve the problem. You can now form a hypothesis based on your observation. The hypothesis may be in a verbal statement or in a mathematical statement.

In a verbal statement, it may be phrased like this:

The nth odd number is the number n plus the number $(n - 1)$.

In a mathematical statement, you may write a formula such as:

The nth odd number $= n + (n - 1) = 2n - 1$.

Notice that the algebraic formula is very neat and easy to use. You can now verify the formula using other data.

Hypothesis Testing

In hypothesis testing, you have to check if the formula or the hypothesis is valid in some other cases. At this stage of the processes, you need to verify that the answer obtained from using the hypothesis/formula or from the sequence of odd numbers is the same in both cases.

You can verify this by checking the 5_{th} odd number. From the sequence of odd numbers 1, 3, 5, 7, 9, ... the 5_{th} odd number is 9. Using the formula, the 5_{th} odd number is worked out as follows:

$$2n - 1 = 2 \times 5 - 1$$
$$= 9$$

Therefore, the answer is the same in both cases.

Next, you can check the 6_{th} odd number. From the sequence of odd numbers 1, 3, 5, 7, 9, 11, ... the 6_{th} odd number is 11. Using the formula, the 6_{th} odd number is worked out as follows:

$$2n - 1 = 2 \times 6 - 1$$
$$= 11$$

The answer is the same in both cases again. You can continue to check a few more cases to make doubly sure your hypothesis/formula is valid. Then you can proceed to make a generalisation.

Generalisation

You can generalise that the nth odd number is $2n - 1$. Using this formula, you can obtain the 304th odd number easily. It is worked out as follows:

$$2n - 1 = 2 \times 304 - 1$$
$$= 607$$

Note: It is more tedious and time-consuming to obtain the answer by listing the odd numbers than by using the formula. In addition, you can use the general formula to find any big odd numbers.

Let's Apply

1. Starting from 1, find the sum of the first 50 odd numbers.

2. Starting from 1, find the sum of the first 100 odd numbers.

3. Starting from 1, find the sum of the first 100 even numbers.

4. Find the number of diagonals in a 99-sided polygon.

7 Use Set Concept

There are some children who encounter difficulties when they are required to solve mathematical problems that involve the concepts of union and intersection of two or more quantities. This is because these two concepts in set are only formally taught to students at the secondary level. However, at the primary level, these two concepts can be deliberately taught to children using the compare and contrast concepts. They can then solve the mathematical problems using the relevant concepts and strategy.

The 'Use Set Concept' strategy can be used to solve mathematical problems that involve the concepts of union and intersection of two or more quantities.

What To Do

Step 1: Identify the items and their quantities in the given problem.

Step 2: Compare and contrast the different quantities of the items or apply the concepts of union and intersection. Solve the problem using equation or diagram where possible.

Example 1

A can with 40 marbles in it has a mass of 135 g. The same can with 20 marbles in it has a mass of 75 g. What is the mass of the can?

Solution

Figure 1 and Figure 2 show the cans with 40 marbles and 20 marbles in it respectively.

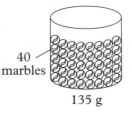 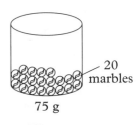

40 marbles

135 g

Fig. 1

20 marbles

75 g

Fig. 2

To solve the problem, you have to write an equation that relates the number of marbles to the mass of marbles. Thus, you have to consider the number of marbles and the mass of marbles separately.

Firstly, compare the 2 cans of marbles. What do they have in common? You will note that every marble is assumed to have the same mass.

Secondly, contrast the 2 cans of marbles. In what ways are they different? You will notice that the first can has 20 more marbles than the second can. Therefore, there is a difference in their masses.

Thirdly, find the mass of 20 marbles. This is done as follows:

$$\text{Difference in the number of marbles} = 40 - 20$$
$$= 20$$
$$\text{Difference in mass between them} = 135 \text{ g} - 75 \text{ g}$$
$$= 60 \text{ g}$$

Equating the number of marbles and its mass, we have:

$$\text{Mass of 20 marbles} = 60 \text{ g}$$

You can now proceed to solve the problem.
The total mass of the second can with 20 marbles = 75 g
Therefore, the mass of the empty can = 75 g – 60 g
$$= 15 \text{ g}$$

Note: When you compare and contrast the two cans of marbles, you are actually applying the set concepts of union and intersection.

Example 2

There are 12 soldiers stationed at a rectangular castle. If there are
4 soldiers on each side of the castle, show how this arrangement is done.

Solution

If you interpret the problem literally and station 4 soldiers on each side
of the castle, you will have 16 soldiers instead of 12 as shown below.

Now, how do you station 12 soldiers instead of 16 soldiers? If you have
acquired set concepts, you will think of sharing (intersection) of soldiers
between the two adjacent sides of the castle. This means you can
actually station 1 soldier at each corner of the rectangle and 2 soldiers
in between two corners as shown below.

Let's Apply

1. There are 7 eggs and 4 baskets. Show how you can arrange 7 eggs in 4 baskets such that each basket has an odd number of eggs.

2. Using 7 coins, show how you can place 3 coins on each side of a triangle.

3. A box with 60 apples in it has a mass of 1220 g. Another identical box with 30 apples in it has a mass of 860 g. If every apple has the same mass, find the mass of the empty box.

4. The mass of a container with 120 cm³ of water is 520 g. The mass of the same container with 40 cm³ of water is 440 g. Find the mass of the empty container.

Part **B**

The Model Approach

There are mathematical problems that can be solved by using different strategies. However, it is important to choose strategies suited to your child's level of understanding. Some strategies are more abstract than others and it can be quite frustrating for you to teach your child to use them.

In this section of the book, you will learn to solve problems using pictorial models. The pictorial model approach is commonly known as 'The Model Approach'.

In the model approach, you use diagrams to represent the problem situations and relevant concepts to help you obtain the answer. Generally, the steps for this approach are as follows:

Step 1: Read and try to understand the question. Then draw bars to represent the problem situations.

Step 2: Label the diagrams with all the relevant information and divide the bars into equal units.

Step 3: Using the diagram, equate the number of units to a quantity to form a proportion statement. The value of the quantity may be given or obtained by computing some given figures in the question.

Step 4: Use unitary or proportion method to get the answer.

The model approach is an important strategy used to solve problems in many topics in primary mathematics. Therefore, this section of the book attempts to cover as many different types of problems as possible that are solved by using the model approach and relevant concepts.

The different concepts covered are as follows:
- Equal Concept
- Comparison Concept
- Difference Concept
- Multiple Concept
- Difference Concept and Multiple Concept
- Making-A-Whole Concept
- Sharing Concept
- Parts-and-Units Concept
- Comparing Fractions Concept

1 Equal Concept

A mathematical concept helps children to understand the procedure instead of just applying the rule to solve problems. Sometimes, children are not able to solve their mathematical problems because they have forgotten the rules. However, if they can understand the concepts, they will be able to work out the answer using the correct strategy.

Examples 1 and 2 show how you may use the equal concept and models (diagrams) to solve problems involving the use of equal concept.

Example 1

In $4 + \underline{\hspace{1.5cm}} = 9$, find the unknown value in the blank.

Solution

Teachers are likely to teach preschoolers how to use the counting-on method to find the unknown value of an equation. For example, in $4 + 6 = \underline{\hspace{1.5cm}}$, they will count from 4 to 10. The answer is 10 because from 5 to 10, there are 6 counters. However, to solve the equation in Example 1, your child needs an alternative strategy as he or she cannot figure out how many counters to use in counting.

You may use the **model approach** to solve it.

In $4 + \underline{\hspace{1.5cm}} = 9$, the equal sign can be interpreted in many ways. For example, it can be interpreted as both sides having the same number of items or length. You can use this concept of equal numbers or lengths to solve the problem. In other words, you can actually use the lengths of bars to represent numbers as shown in the model on page 41.

Note: An equation has an equal sign that relates the left-hand statement to the right-hand statement.

The model is drawn as follows.

4	?

9

From the model, you can see that the longer bar has the same length as the sum of the 2 shorter bars. Therefore, to find the length of the unknown shorter bar, you need to subtract 4 from 9.

$$\underline{\hspace{2cm}} = 9 - 4 = 5$$

The unknown value is 5.

Notice that the original equation has been transformed into a length model. From the length model, it is interpreted as a simple subtraction equation which your child should have no problem solving.

Example 2

In $9 - \underline{\hspace{2cm}} = 6$, find the unknown value in the blank.

Solution

Similarly, you can use the same equal concept and interpret the subtraction equation in Example 2 using the bars shown below.

9

6	?

From the model, you will notice that the first bar has a length of 9 units. The second bar has a length of 6 units added to a bar of unknown units. If the bar of unknown units is subtracted from the bar of 9 units, the remaining bar has 6 units left. Here, you use the concept of taking away for subtraction. Next, you reinterpret the model as a simpler addition or subtraction operation. From the model, the unknown value is given by $9 - 6$.

$$\underline{\hspace{2cm}} = 9 - 6 = 3$$

The unknown value is 3.

Let's Apply

Draw models to solve the following problems.

1. Find the missing number in the blank in the addition equation.

$$8 + \underline{\hspace{1.5cm}} = 15$$

2. Find the missing number in the blank in the addition equation.

$$\underline{\hspace{1.5cm}} + 9 = 17$$

3. Find the missing number in the blank in the subtraction equation.

$$16 - \underline{\hspace{1.5cm}} = 8$$

4. Find the missing number in the blank in the subtraction equation.

$$\underline{\hspace{1.5cm}} - 4 = 7$$

2 Comparison Concept

Children at the lower primary level often encounter problems on comparison of numbers. Examples of such problems are '7 more than 15 is _____' and '7 less than 15 is _____'. Some children might find these mathematical statements abstract and rely on cue words like 'more than is add' and 'less than is minus' to help them get the answers. However, this cue-word strategy is not robust because it does not work all the time. You can teach your child to use the model approach instead as it is a more reliable strategy.

Examples 1 to 6 show how the model approach is used to solve problems such as the following:

(1) 7 **more than** 15 is _____.

(2) 7 **less than** 15 is _____.

(3) 7 **more than** _____ is 22.

(4) _____ **more than** 15 is 22.

(5) 6 **less than** _____ is 8.

(6) _____ **less than** 15 is 8.

Example 1

Find the unknown value in the blank.

7 more than 15 is _____.

Solution

Using the model approach, you translate the mathematical statement into a more concrete representation first. This can be done using a bar diagram. The statement '7 more than 15' means '7 is added on to 15'. The resulting number must therefore be bigger than the starting number 15.

You will notice that 15 is the number after the words 'more than'. You can then proceed to draw a bar that represents the starting number 15. Next, you can draw a shorter bar to represent 7 which is added on to 15 as shown below.

resulting bar

From the model, you will notice that an arrow is drawn above the bar that represents 7. This is done to show the concept of 'adding on'. The resulting bar is the sum of the two numbers and it represents the answer to the problem which is worked out as follows:

$$\text{_____} = 15 + 7 = 22$$

The unknown value is 22.

In summary, the whole procedure in solving the problem involves the following:

(1) translate the mathematical statement into a model first

(2) interpret the model and translate it into a simpler mathematical statement (_____ = 15 + 7) to obtain the answer

Note: To apply this method, you need to identify the starting number to draw the first bar. This number is always the one immediately after the words 'more than' or 'less than'.

Example 2

What is the missing number in the blank?

7 less than 15 is ―――――.

Solution

In this example, the words 'less than' means 'is subtracted from'. Therefore, '7 less than 15' means '7 is subtracted from 15'. Having understood this basic concept of 'less than', you can proceed to solve the problem using the same strategy as Example 1.

Firstly, you need to identify the starting number to draw the first bar. In this case, the number is 15. Next, you need to draw a bar that represents 7 which is subtracted from 15. Finally, you have to draw a bar of unknown value to complete the whole bar as shown below.

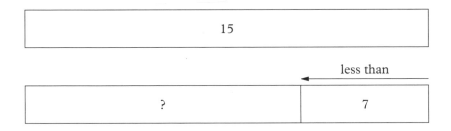

Now, you can interpret the model you have drawn and translate it into a simple equation as follows:

$$\text{――――――} = 15 - 7$$
$$= 8$$

The missing number is 8.

Examples 1 and 2 show only one variation of a set of possible problems that your children may encounter. However, questions may be varied which require your children to draw slightly different diagrams as shown in Example 3 to Example 6.

Example 3

What is the unknown value in the blank?

7 more than _____ is 22.

Solution

You can draw bars to represent the above statement and solve the problem.

?	7

22

From the model, you can write down the following equation.

$$_\_\_\_\_ = 22 - 7$$
$$= 15$$

The unknown value is 15.

Note: In this example, you will notice that the cue words 'more than is add' do not apply as you have to subtract 7 from 22 to get the answer.

Example 4

What is the unknown value in the blank?

_____ more than 15 is 22.

Solution

You can draw the bars as follows:

From the model, you can write down the following equation.

$$\underline{} = 22 - 15$$
$$= 7$$

The unknown value is 7.

Note: The cue words 'more than is add' do not apply in this case. You have to subtract 15 from 22 to get the answer.

Example 5

What is the unknown value in the blank?

6 less than _____ is 8.

Solution

You can draw the bars as follows:

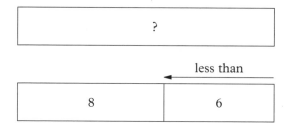

From the model, you can write down the following equation.

$$\underline{\hspace{2cm}} = 8 + 6$$
$$= 14$$

The unknown value is 14.

Note: The cue words 'less than is minus' do not apply in this case as you have to add 6 to 8 to get the answer.

Example 6

What is the unknown value in the blank?

_____ less than 15 is 8.

Solution

You can draw the bars as follows:

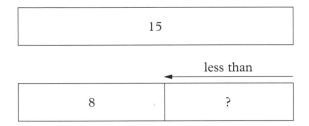

From the model, you can write down the following equation.

$$\text{_____} = 15 - 8$$
$$= 7$$

The unknown value is 7.

In this example, you have to subtract 8 from 15 to get the answer. Therefore, your children should not use the cue-word strategy to solve problems on comparison of numbers as it is not a reliable method. They should learn to use the model approach instead.

Let's Apply

Draw models to solve the following problems.

1. What is the unknown value in the blank?
   9 more than 14 is _____.

2. What is the unknown value in the blank?
   6 more than _____ is 21.

3. What is the unknown value in the blank?
   _____ more than 12 is 25.

4. What is the unknown value in the blank?
   9 less than 14 is _____.

5. What is the unknown value in the blank?
   6 less than _____ is 20.

6. What is the unknown value in the blank?
   _____ less than 23 is 15.

3 Difference Concept

Non-routine problems where the price or quantity of one item is less than or more than that of another involve the difference concept. When you apply the difference concept, you subtract the smaller number from the bigger number. Sometimes, you may use algebra to solve mathematical problems that involve the difference concept.

However, there are children at the primary level who have not learned how to form or solve algebraic equations. They have not reached the formal operational level to help them understand the concepts used in algebra. As such, it is better for them to use the model approach instead as it is less abstract.

Examples 1 and 2 show how you can use the model approach to solve problems that involve the difference concept.

Example 1

A plate of chicken rice and a bowl of noodles cost $8. The bowl of noodles cost $2 more than the plate of chicken rice. Find the cost of the bowl of noodles.

Solution

You can use algebra and the model approach to solve the problem and see for yourself which is the simpler method for your children to adopt.

There are 2 items in the given problem, chicken rice and noodles. The difference in price between the 2 items is $2. You can use x and y to represent the cost of a plate of chicken rice and the cost of a bowl of noodles respectively and form two algebraic equations as follows:

$$x + y = 8 \quad \dots\dots\dots\dots\dots \ (1)$$

$$y - x = 2 \quad \dots\dots\dots\dots\dots \ (2)$$

When you solve for x and y, you will get $x = 3$ and $y = 5$. That is, a plate of chicken rice costs $3 and a bowl of noodles costs $5.

If you use the model approach, you will need to draw bars to show the relationship between the cost of a plate of chicken rice and a bowl of noodles. The bars can be drawn as follows:

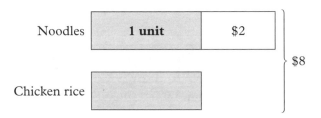

The longer bar represents the cost of a bowl of noodles and the shaded shorter bar represents the cost of a plate of chicken rice and it is denoted as 1 unit.

From the model,

$$2 \text{ units} \longrightarrow \$8 - \$2 = \$6$$

$$1 \text{ unit} \longrightarrow \$3$$

The plate of chicken rice costs $3.

$$1 \text{ unit} + \$2 \longrightarrow \$5$$

The bowl of noodles costs $5.

In summary, to apply the model approach, you need to translate the statements in the question into a model first. Next, you have to interpret the model and form an equation that relates the number of units to $6. Then you can apply the unitary or proportion concept to find the answer.

Example 2

The total cost of an apple, an orange and a pear is $2. A pear costs 70 cents more than an apple. An orange costs 20 cents less than an apple. Find the cost of the pear.

Solution

Firstly, you have to translate the statements in the question into a model. In this case, you will have to draw 3 bars to represent the cost of a pear, an apple and an orange respectively as follows:

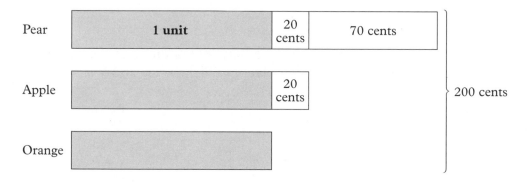

From the model, you can see that the shaded parts of the bars are equal in length and they represent 1 unit each. Usually, the smallest value (in this case the cost of the orange) is taken as 1 unit.

Secondly, you have to interpret the model and form an equation that relates the number of units to a quantity. The value of the quantity may be obtained by computing some given figures in the question.

From the model, you can compute the cost of a pear by adding 1 unit, 20 cents and 70 cents. You can compute the cost of an apple by adding 1 unit and 20 cents. The cost of the orange is represented by 1 unit. The $2 is converted to 200 cents.

$$3 \text{ units} \longrightarrow (200 - 20 - 20 - 70) \text{ cents} = 90 \text{ cents}$$

$$1 \text{ unit} \longrightarrow 30 \text{ cents}$$

$(30 + 20 + 70) = 120$ cents

The cost of the pear is $1.20.

Let's Apply

Draw models to solve the following problems.

1. The total cost of a cake and a doughnut is $1.20. The doughnut costs 20 cents more than the cake. Find the cost of the doughnut.

2. The total cost of a Mathematics book and an English book is $27. The Mathematics book costs $3 more than the English book. Find the cost of the Mathematics book.

3. The total cost of a burger, a drink and a salad is $6. The burger costs $1 more than the salad and the drink costs $1 less than the salad. Find the cost of the burger.

4. Mrs Cheong bought a book, a bag and a pen for her son. The total cost was $32. The book cost $4 less than the bag. The bag cost $12 more than the pen. Find the cost of the bag.

4 Multiple Concept

The multiple concept is concerned with the number of times each quantity is as much as the other quantity. This concept is related to the difference concept. The model approach may be used to solve problems that involve the multiple concept. Some of the mathematical terms your children will encounter in such problems are 'twice as much as' and 'three times the age of'.

The following example shows how the model approach is used to solve such problems.

Example

Ann is twice as old as Bill. Bill is three times as old as Carol. If their total age is 70 years old, how old is Bill?

Solution

Firstly, you have to translate the statements in the question into a model. You can draw bars to represent the ages of the three people. The bar that represents Ann's age is twice the length of the bar that represents Bill's age because she is twice as old as Bill . The bar that represents Carol's age is one-third the length of the bar that represents Bill's age because Bill is three times as old as Carol.

Secondly, you have to divide the bars into smaller units. The shortest bar is taken as one unit. Therefore, Ann's bar is divided into 6 units, Bill's bar is divided into 3 units and Carol's bar is one unit.

The 3 bars can be drawn as follows:

Thirdly, you have to translate the model into an equation that relates the number of units to the quantity, 70.

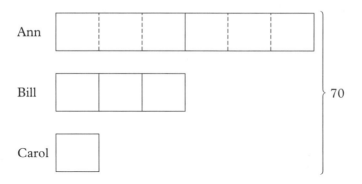

From the model, you will notice that the total number of units is 10. You can then proceed to find the value represented by 1 unit and 3 units (Bill's age).

$$10 \text{ units} \longrightarrow 70 \text{ years old}$$

$$1 \text{ unit} \longrightarrow 7 \text{ years old}$$

$$3 \text{ units} \longrightarrow (3 \times 7) = 21 \text{ years old}$$

Bill is 21 years old.

Let's Apply

1. Joseph sold twice as many oranges as Larry. Larry sold three times as many oranges as Peter. If they sold 150 oranges altogether, how many oranges did Joseph sell?

2. Tom has 3 times the number of marbles as Sally. Sally has twice as many marbles as Tina. They have 180 marbles in all. How many marbles does Tom have?

5 Difference Concept And Multiple Concept

There are mathematical problems that involve both the difference and multiple concepts. Similarly, your children may use the model approach to solve such problems. They have to use the concepts separately when they draw the model.

The following example shows the use of both concepts in a problem and how the model approach is used to solve it.

Example

Xiaozheng is twice as tall as Yenfen. Yenfen is 32 cm shorter than Zhengli. Their total height is 480 cm. Find the height of Zhengli.

Solution

The statement, 'twice as tall as' is a multiple concept and the statement, 'shorter than' is a difference concept. Using these 2 concepts and other relevant information, the model can be drawn as follows:

Xiaozheng		
Yenfen		
Zhengli		32 cm

480 cm

Notice that the bars are divided into smaller units. Since Yenfen is the shortest, you can use 1 unit to represent her height.

From the model, you can work out the value represented by 1 unit and Zhengli's height as follows:

$$4 \text{ units} \longrightarrow (480 - 32) = 448 \text{ cm}$$

$$1 \text{ unit} \longrightarrow 112 \text{ cm}$$

$$1 \text{ unit} + 32 \text{ cm} \longrightarrow (112 + 32) = 144 \text{ cm}$$

The height of Zhengli is 144 cm.

Let's Apply

1. Joseph sold twice as many oranges as Larry. Peter sold 25 more oranges than Larry. If they sold 85 oranges altogether, how many oranges did each person sell?

2. Tina has three times as many marbles as Sally. Sally has 40 marbles less than Tom. They have 120 marbles in all. How many marbles does each person have?

6 Making-A-Whole Concept

In the previous sections, you have been given some problems that allow you to identify equal parts easily so that you can form an equation relating the number of units to a certain quantity. In the example given below, you will not be able to solve it using only the previous concepts. You need to use the 'Making-A-Whole Concept' strategy to identify equal parts to form an equation. The basic concept used here is to extend a bar to make one whole.

The following example shows how this concept and the model approach can be used to solve problems.

Example

Jane collected three times as many pebbles as Karen. Gina collected 21 pebbles less than Jane. They collected 427 pebbles altogether. How many pebbles did Gina collect?

Solution

Using the model approach, you can draw the bars as follows:

From the model, notice that if you assign 1 unit to represent the number of pebbles collected by Karen, you will not be able to figure out the number of units that represent Gina's pebbles. To resolve this problem, you need to extend the length of the bar that represents Gina's pebbles and make it the same length as the bar that represents Jane's pebbles. That is, you are extending Gina's bar to make one whole. In this case, Jane's bar is taken as one whole.

Jane			

Karen	

Gina			

427 + 21
= 448 pebbles

Now, using the new model, if you take the length of Karen's bar as 1 unit, the total number of units for the three bars is 3 + 1 + 3 = 7. You must also remember that you have added 21 pebbles to Gina's collection so that the number of pebbles is the same as Jane's. Therefore, the total number of pebbles is 427 + 21 = 448.

You can then proceed to work out the number of pebbles represented by 1 unit and the number of pebbles collected by Gina as follows:

$$7 \text{ units} \longrightarrow (427 + 21) = 448 \text{ pebbles}$$
$$1 \text{ unit} \longrightarrow 64 \text{ pebbles}$$
$$3 \text{ units} \longrightarrow (3 \times 64) = 192 \text{ pebbles}$$
$$3 \text{ units} - 21 \text{ pebbles} \longrightarrow (192 - 21) = 171 \text{ pebbles}$$

Gina collected 171 pebbles.

Notice that the problem is easily solved by using the 'Making-A-Whole' concept and the model approach.

Let's Apply

1. Ronnie sold twice as many chocolates as Ben. Ken sold 40 chocolates less than Ben. If all of them sold 628 chocolates altogether, how many chocolates did each person sell?

2. Allen has twice as many marbles as George. Dawn has 28 marbles less than Allen. If they have 242 marbles altogether, how many marbles does each person have?

7 Sharing Concept

A type of mathematical problem that your children may encounter involves the concept of sharing quantities. In such problems, two sets of quantities are rearranged such that one set is decreased while the other set is increased with no change in the total quantity.

Many children who are operating at the concrete level in their mental thinking have difficulty conceptualising the changes. Therefore, it is better to use models to help them visualise the changes in the 'before-and-after' situations.

Examples 1 and 2 show how the model approach is applied to solve this type of problem.

Example 1

Samy had 198 sweets and Zainal had 74 sweets. Samy gave Zainal some sweets so that both had the same number of sweets.

(a) How many sweets did Samy have at the end?

(b) How many sweets did Samy give Zainal?

Solution

For this type of problems, you need to highlight to your children the total number of sweets will not change. They have to bear this point in mind when they draw the model to represent the changes from one situation to another.

The bars can be drawn as follows:

Before

Samy	198 sweets

272 sweets

Zainal	74 sweets

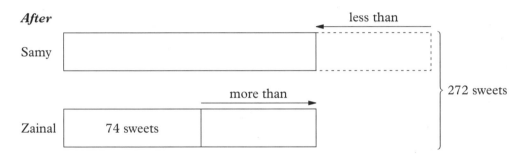

Since the total number of sweets is the same in both situations, the total length of the bars in both cases must be the same. The total number of sweets is the sum of 198 and 74 sweets or 272 sweets.

Notice that the second model represents the situation where both boys have the same number of sweets. If each bar in this model represents one unit, then you can work out the number of sweets each boy has as follows:

(a) 2 units $\longrightarrow$ (198 + 74) = 272 sweets

   1 unit $\longrightarrow$ 136 sweets

Samy had 136 sweets at the end.

At the beginning, Samy had 198 sweets. At the end, he had 136 sweets. Therefore, the difference between the number of sweets represents the number of sweets given by Samy to Zainal. It is worked out as follows:

(b) 198 – 136 = 62

Samy gave Zainal 62 sweets.

Example 2

Samy had 198 sweets and Zainal had 74 sweets. Samy gave Zainal some sweets so that he had 12 more sweets than Zainal at the end.

(a) How many sweets did Samy have at the end?

(b) How many sweets did Samy give Zainal?

Solution

You can draw a model to represent the situation at the end as follows:

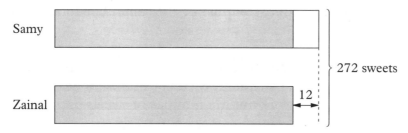

Note that the total number of sweets is the same regardless of the number of sweets given to Zainal. If the shaded parts in the model represent 2 units, you can work out the number of sweets represented by 1 unit and therefore, the number of sweets each boy has at the end.

From the model,

$$2 \text{ units} \longrightarrow (272 - 12) = 260 \text{ sweets}$$
$$1 \text{ unit} \longrightarrow 130 \text{ sweets}$$

(a) 1 unit + 12 sweets $\longrightarrow (130 + 12) = 142$ sweets

Samy had 142 sweets at the end.

Next, you can make a comparison between the number of sweets Samy had before and after he had given them to Zainal. The bars below represent the two situations. The difference in the number of sweets represents the number of sweets given by Samy to Zainal.

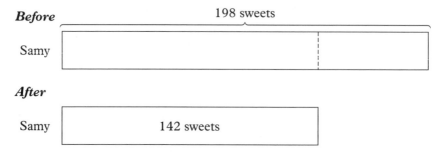

(b) From the model,

(198 – 142) sweets = 56 sweets

Samy gave 56 sweets to Zainal so that he had 12 more sweets than Zainal. Notice that Zainal had (74 + 56) sweets or 130 sweets.

In summary, the few points you need to take note of in order to solve such problems are as follows:

(1) The total quantity of an item remains the same before and after an event has taken place.

(2) A model has to be drawn to represent the situation after an event has taken place.

(3) The number of items given is the same as the number of items received.

Let's Apply

1. Box A and Box B contained 154 and 72 oranges respectively. Ronnie transferred some oranges from Box A into Box B so that both boxes had the same number of oranges.
    (a) How many oranges were there in each box finally?
    (b) How many oranges did Ronnie transfer from Box A into Box B?

2. Meimei and Huihui had 98 cards and 164 cards respectively. Huihui gave some cards to Meimei. If both girls had the same number of cards at the end, find
    (a) how many cards each girl had at the end,
    (b) how many cards Huihui gave to Meimei.

3. Box A and Box B contained 154 oranges and 72 oranges respectively. Ronnie transferred some oranges from Box A into Box B so that Box A had 24 more oranges than Box B at the end.
    (a) How many oranges were there in each box finally?
    (b) How many oranges did Ronnie transfer from Box A into Box B?

4. Meimei and Huihui had 98 cards and 164 cards respectively. Huihui gave some cards to Meimei. If Meimei had 10 more cards than Huihui at the end, find
    (a) how many cards each girl had at the end,
    (b) how many cards Huihui gave to Meimei.

8 Parts-And-Units Concept

Complex mathematical problems on fractions can be simplified and solved using the model approach. Your children may find this topic on fractions abstract and have difficulty grasping some of its concepts. Sometimes, they wrongly apply the concepts on whole numbers to problems in fractions. For example, when they are required to add or subtract two fractions, they actually add or subtract the numerators in the same way as whole numbers without considering the denominator.

You can only add or subtract two numerators as given when the fractions come from a single whole number. If two fractions come from different whole numbers, then each fraction unit from the two fractions is not the same and therefore, they cannot be added or subtracted like whole numbers.

Examples 1 and 2 show how the model approach is used to solve more complex problems on fractions that involve using the parts-and-units concept.

Example 1

Janice had \$480. She spent $\frac{2}{3}$ of it on a watch and $\frac{1}{4}$ of the remainder on a pen. How much money had she left?

Solution

Notice that the two fractions in the question do not come from the same whole number. $\frac{2}{3}$ of the amount is computed from Janice's original sum of money. $\frac{1}{4}$ of the amount is computed from the remaining sum of money. Therefore, each unit from these two fractions does not have the same value. You have to convert them into the same unit so that you can add or subtract the units. A model will be useful in this case as it can help you to solve your problem.

You can draw the bars as follows:

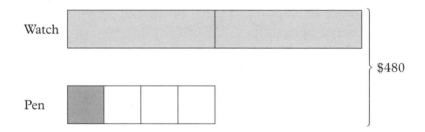

Convert into the same unit:

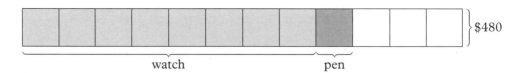

From the model, you can see how $\frac{2}{3}$ (lighter shaded part) of the whole

sum of money and $\frac{1}{4}\left(\text{shaded part of } \frac{1}{3}\right)$ of the remainder are

represented using the bars.

The whole sum of money is divided into 3 parts and each part of the money is divided into 4 units. In total, there are 3×4 units or 12 units altogether. You can then proceed to find the amount of money represented by 1 unit and hence solve the problem as follows:

$$\text{Total number of units spent} = 2 \text{ parts} + 1 \text{ unit}$$
$$= (2 \times 4 + 1)$$
$$= 9$$

$$\text{Total number of units not spent} = 3$$
$$12 \text{ units} \longrightarrow \$480$$
$$1 \text{ unit} \longrightarrow \$40$$
$$3 \text{ units} \longrightarrow \$120$$

She had $120 left.

Example 2

2 pears cost as much as 3 apples. If the total cost of 2 apples and 5 pears is $5.70, find the cost of each fruit.

Solution

Since 2 pears cost as much as 3 apples, the bars you draw to represent the cost of 3 apples and 2 pears respectively should be the same. You can draw the bars as follows:

Apples

Pears

From the above model, you will notice that the number of parts in each bar is different. Therefore the value represented by each part in each bar is not the same. To solve the problem, you have to convert the parts for each bar into equal units as shown below.

Apples

3 parts = 6 units
1 part = 2 units
1 part (for apple) = 2 units

Pears

2 parts = 6 units
1 part = 3 units
1 part (for pear) = 3 units

You can proceed to find the cost represented by 1 unit and hence solve the problem as follows:

$$3 \text{ units} \longrightarrow 1 \text{ pear}$$
$$2 \text{ units} \longrightarrow 1 \text{ apple}$$

Cost of 2 apples and 5 pears is $5.70.

$$4 \text{ units} \longrightarrow 2 \text{ apples}$$
$$15 \text{ units} \longrightarrow 5 \text{ pears}$$

(4 + 15) units or 19 units represent the cost of 2 apples and 5 pears.

$$19 \text{ units} \longrightarrow \$5.70$$
$$1 \text{ unit} \longrightarrow \$0.30$$
$$2 \text{ units} \longrightarrow \$0.60$$
$$3 \text{ units} \longrightarrow \$0.90$$

The cost of 1 apple is $0.60 and the cost of 1 pear is $0.90.

Let's Apply

1. Johnny had 240 marbles. He gave $\frac{3}{4}$ of them to his brothers. Of the remainder, he gave $\frac{1}{3}$ to his friends. How many marbles had he left?

2. Dr Sen saw 150 patients in one day. In the morning, he saw $\frac{4}{5}$ of his patients. In the afternoon, he saw $\frac{1}{3}$ of the remaining number of patients. He saw the rest of the patients in the evening. How many patients did he see in the evening?

3. The cost of 10 doughnuts and 2 cakes is the same. If the cost of 3 cakes and 5 doughnuts is $8, find the cost of each item.

4. The mass of 2 cups and 3 mugs is 690 g. If the mass of 5 cups is the same as that of 4 mugs, find the mass of each item.

9 Comparing Fractions Concept

One of the ways your children can compare two sets of items is to find the difference in the number of items between them. They can also compare two sets of items by weighing them separately and then note the difference between the two masses. In these two cases, comparison is made using countable sets and masses respectively. It is always easier to compare two sets of items using whole numbers rather than fractions.

The following example shows how the model approach is used to solve one type of problems that involves comparison between different items using the concept of fraction.

Example

Xiaoming's mass is $\frac{1}{2}$ the mass of Yenfen. Zhangli is $\frac{2}{3}$ as heavy as Xiaoming. If Yenfen's mass is 48 kg, find the masses of Xiaoming and Zhangli.

Solution

The first statement in the question is straightforward and most children have no problem understanding it. They will know that Yenfen is heavier than Xiaoming and her mass is twice Xiaoming's mass.

You can draw a model to represent their masses as follows:

However, some children may not be able to understand and interpret the second statement. They may wonder who is heavier, Zhangli or Xiaoming? You can explain this statement to your child by using the instrumental approach. That is, you can use a rule to help your child draw a model to represent the relationship between Zhangli's mass and Xiaoming's mass. From the statement 'Zhangli is $\frac{2}{3}$ as heavy as Xiaoming', you can draw 2 units (numerator 2) to represent Zhangli's mass and 3 units (denominator 3) to represent Xiaoming's mass. Therefore, you can draw the three bars to represent each person's mass as follows:

Yenfen — 48 kg

Xiaoming

Zhangli

From the model, you can proceed to find out the mass represented by 1 unit of the bar and hence solve the problem as follows:

$$6 \text{ units} \longrightarrow 48 \text{ kg}$$
$$1 \text{ unit} \longrightarrow 8 \text{ kg}$$
$$2 \text{ units} \longrightarrow 16 \text{ kg}$$
$$3 \text{ units} \longrightarrow 24 \text{ kg}$$

Xiaoming's mass is 24 kg and Zhangli's mass is 16 kg.

Let's Apply

1. Abu had $\frac{1}{4}$ as many stamps as Bakar. Bakar had $\frac{2}{3}$ as many stamps as Harun. If Harun had 24 stamps, how many stamps had each of the other two boys?

2. Shanti's salary is $\frac{3}{4}$ of John's salary. Jamie's salary is $\frac{1}{3}$ of Shanti's salary. If John's salary is $840, how much does each of the other two earn?

Challenging Examination Problems

In Part A and Part B of this book, you have learnt many different strategies that can be used to solve mathematical problems encountered by pupils from primary four to six.

In Part C, you will learn to apply strategies to solve challenging examination problems encountered by primary five and six pupils. These examination problems prepare pupils for similar challenging PSLE problems.

The strategies used in this section are as follows:
- Use Model Approach and Make Inferences
- Use Model Approach and Part-Whole Concept
- Use Model Approach and Changing Ratio Concept
- Use Model Approach and Guess and Check Strategy
- Use Model Approach and Replacement Concept
- Use Make A List Strategy

1 Use Model Approach And Make Inferences

Most children have come across many types of problems on fractions. One type involves fractions taken from different wholes. You can teach your child to use the model approach and make inferences to solve such problems.

Generally, the 4 stages of the model approach are as follows:

(1) translate the mathematical statements given in the problem into a model

(2) modify the model into parts and/or equal parts

(3) make inferences and form an equation that relates the number of units or parts to a quantity

(4) use unitary or proportion method to complete the solution

The following example on fractions taken from different wholes is solved by the '4-stage model' and making correct inferences from the statements given.

Example

David read 32 pages of a book for his assignment on Monday. On Tuesday, he read $\frac{1}{6}$ of the remaining pages. Find how many more pages he had to read if he had read only $\frac{1}{2}$ the number of pages in the book.

Solution

Firstly, translate the statements into a model. In the process of doing this, you need to note that there are 2 fractions given in this problem and they are from 2 different wholes. The fraction $\frac{1}{6}$ is from a whole that represents the remaining number of pages. The fraction $\frac{1}{2}$ is from a whole that represents the total number of pages.

Based on the given information, you can draw the model as follows:

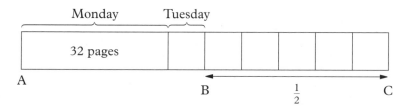

Since $\frac{1}{6}$ of the remaining pages are read on Tuesday, you can divide the length of the bar that represents these remaining pages into 6 smaller equal units as shown in the model.

From the statements in the question, you can make the following inferences:

(1) out of the 6 units that represent the remaining pages, 5 units are not read

(2) $\frac{1}{2}$ of the book consists of 32 pages and $\frac{1}{6}$ of the remaining pages

(3) $\frac{1}{2}$ of the book is represented by 5 units which is actually $\frac{5}{6}$ of the remaining pages

(4) the total number of pages in the book is represented by 10 units

(5) the number of pages read on Monday is represented by $(10 - 6)$ or 4 units

(6) $\frac{4}{10}$ of the total number of pages equal 32 pages

From the inferences and the model, you can work out the number of pages represented by 1 unit and hence solve the problem as follows:

$$5 \text{ units (BC)} \longrightarrow \frac{1}{2} \text{ of the total number of pages in the book}$$
$$10 \text{ units (AC)} \longrightarrow \text{the total number of pages in the book}$$

On Monday, David read 32 pages which is represented by $(10 - 6)$ units.

$$4 \text{ units} \longrightarrow 32 \text{ pages}$$
$$1 \text{ unit} \longrightarrow \frac{32}{4} \text{ or 8 pages}$$
$$5 \text{ units} \longrightarrow 40 \text{ pages}$$

He had to read 40 more pages.

Let's Apply

1. Lijun gave 28 of her beads to Chunlian. Of the remaining beads, she lost $\frac{2}{5}$ of them. If she had $\frac{1}{2}$ of the total number of beads left, find how many beads she had at the beginning.

2. Hassan spent $15 of his money on durians and $\frac{1}{4}$ of the remainder on oranges. If he had $\frac{1}{3}$ of his money left, how much did he have at first?

2 Use Model Approach And Part-Whole Concept

You have learnt how to solve problems involving fractions from different wholes using the model approach and making inferences. In this section, you will learn how to solve problems that involve fractions taken from the same whole. This type of problems can be solved using the model approach and the part-whole concept as shown in the following example.

Example

Mrs Chen had a box of candies. She gave $\frac{1}{3}$ of the candies to the pupils in Class A and 35 candies to those in Class B. She then had $\frac{1}{4}$ of the original number of candies left. If she packed the remaining candies in bags of 5 each,

(a) how many candies had she at the beginning?

(b) how many bags did she use?

Solution

First of all, you have to translate the statements into a model. From the statements, you will know that the fractions $\frac{1}{3}$ and $\frac{1}{4}$ are taken from the same whole (total number of candies). Also, from the same whole, 35 candies were given to the pupils in Class B. Thus, the model can be drawn as follows:

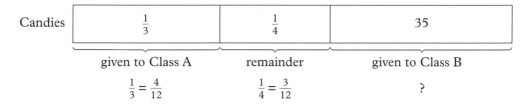

Notice that there are two number representations shown in the above part-whole diagram. They are 35 candies and the number of candies represented by the fractional parts $\frac{1}{3}$ and $\frac{1}{4}$. To find the original number of candies, you need to know the fractional part that represents 35 candies.

(a) The fractional part that represents 35 candies can be obtained using the concept of part and whole as follows:

From the model, $1 - \dfrac{1}{3} - \dfrac{1}{4} = 1 - \dfrac{4}{12} - \dfrac{3}{12}$

$$= \dfrac{5}{12}$$

Therefore, $\dfrac{5}{12}$ of the total number of sweets is 35 sweets.

Next, using the unit concept for model, you can divide the bar into 12 equal units and equate 5 units with 35 candies as shown below. Then you can proceed to find the number of candies represented by 1 unit and hence the total number of candies.

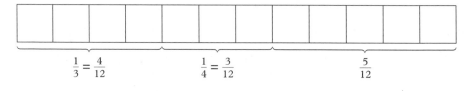

$$\dfrac{1}{3} = \dfrac{4}{12} \qquad \dfrac{1}{4} = \dfrac{3}{12} \qquad \dfrac{5}{12}$$

$$5 \text{ units} \longrightarrow 35 \text{ candies}$$
$$1 \text{ unit} \longrightarrow 7 \text{ candies}$$
$$12 \text{ units} \longrightarrow 12 \times 7 = 84 \text{ candies}$$

Therefore, she had 84 candies at the beginning.

(b) To find the number of bags she used for packing the remaining candies, you need to find the number of candies that were not given away. From the statement, you know that she had $\dfrac{1}{4}$ of the original number of candies left.

$$\dfrac{1}{4} = \dfrac{3}{12}$$
$$1 \text{ unit} \longrightarrow 7 \text{ candies}$$
$$3 \text{ units} \longrightarrow 3 \times 7 = 21 \text{ candies}$$
$$\dfrac{21}{5} = 4\dfrac{1}{5}$$

Therefore, she used 5 bags.

Note: When you teach your child to solve challenging problems on fractions, you have to explain to them the differences between each type of problems.

Let's Apply

1. Mrs Quek made some cakes. She sold $\frac{1}{3}$ of them and gave 14 pieces to her children. Then she was left with $\frac{1}{5}$ of the cakes she had made. She packed all the remaining cakes into some boxes. If each box contained 4 cakes,
   (a) how many cakes did she bake?
   (b) how many boxes did she use?

2. Rahman had some pears. He sold $\frac{2}{3}$ of them to Kanan and gave 8 pears to John. Then he had $\frac{1}{4}$ of his pears left. If he put the remaining pears in bags of 5 each,
   (a) how many pears did he have at the beginning?
   (b) how many bags did he use?

3 Use Model Approach And Changing Ratio Concept

There are different types of problems on ratios. Your children would have encountered several of these problems. They can be solved using the 4-stage model approach. In this section, you will learn how to solve problems that involve changes in the ratios of two quantities. The model changes when there is a change in the ratio of the quantities.

The following example shows how the model approach is used to solve such problems on changing ratios.

Example 1

May and June had beads in the ratio 3 : 4. May bought 48 more beads. The additional number of beads June bought is $\frac{1}{4}$ of her original number of beads. If both girls had the same number of beads, find the total number of beads they had finally.

Solution

Firstly, you have to draw a model based on the statements given in the example. The bars below represent the number of beads each girl had at first.

Before

May

June

} ? beads

Secondly, draw to show the changes in the model when both girls bought more beads. Your model must show that both girls had the same number of beads as given in the statement. Therefore, both bars have the same length now as shown below.

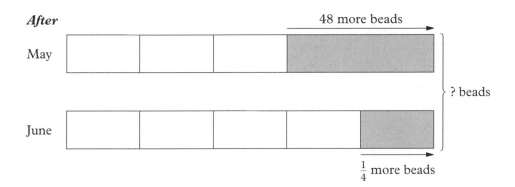

Thirdly, you have to equate the number of units with 48 beads and solve the problem using the unitary method.

From the model,   2 units ⟶ 48 beads
                    1 unit ⟶ 24 beads
                    10 units ⟶ 240 beads

Therefore, they had 240 beads finally.

The following example is a higher order problem on changing ratios where you have to make more rigorous inferences from the models.

Example 2

The ratio of the number of chickens to the number of ducks in a farm was 1 : 4. Mr Brown bought 36 more chickens. At the same time, he sold 36 ducks. If he had as many chickens as ducks finally,

(a) how many ducks did he have at the beginning?

(b) how many ducks and chickens did he have in all at the end?

Solution

As usual, you have to draw a model to represent the problem situation before the ratio of the two quantities changes. The bars can be drawn as follows:

Before

Chickens

Ducks

? chickens and ducks

Since there are 4 times as many ducks as chickens, the number of ducks is represented by 4 units and the number of chickens is represented by 1 unit in the model. Thus, the difference in the number of ducks and chickens is represented by $(4 - 1)$ units.

Next, you have to draw a model to show the changes in the ratio from 1 : 4 to 1 : 1 after Mr Brown bought 36 chickens and sold 36 ducks. Since the number of chickens bought is the same as the number of ducks sold, the length of the bar that represents each number is the same as shown below.

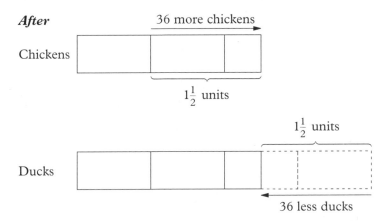

Note that the total number of chickens and ducks is represented by 5 units as before. This is because the increase in the number of chickens is offset by the decrease in the number of ducks. Therefore, in this new model, 36 chickens or 36 ducks are represented by $1\frac{1}{2}$ units. The two bars have the same length now to reflect the new ratio, 1 : 1.

From the model, you can work out the number of chickens or ducks that is represented by 1 unit of the bar and hence solve the problem as follows:

$$3 \text{ units} \longrightarrow 72$$
$$1 \text{ unit} \longrightarrow 24$$
$$4 \text{ units} \longrightarrow 4 \times 24 = 96$$
$$5 \text{ units} \longrightarrow 5 \times 24 = 120$$

(a) He had 96 ducks at the beginning.

(b) He had 120 ducks and chickens in all at the end.

In summary, for this type of problems, remember that you have to draw two models to show the changes in the ratios of the quantities and then make inferences to relate the number of units to the correct quantities and solve it.

Let's Apply

1. Jiali had thrice as many marbles as Minsen. Jiali doubled the number of marbles he had in three months. Minsen increased the number of marbles he had by 85 in the same period. If they had the same number of marbles at the end, how many marbles did they have altogether then?

2. Bottle A and Bottle B contained water in the ratio 3 : 2. Mr Chiam poured 0.5 ℓ of water into Bottle A and 2.1 ℓ of water into Bottle B. If both bottles contained the same volume of water, how many litres of water were there finally?

3. Mr Hosni had cows and goats in the ratio 2 : 5. He sold 30 goats and bought 30 cows. If he had as many cows as goats finally,
   (a) how many cows had he at the beginning?
   (b) how many cows and goats had he altogether at the end?

4. The ratio of basketballs to volleyballs in a basket is 5 : 1. 24 basketballs are removed from the basket. At the same time, 24 volleyballs are added to the other balls in the basket. If there are as many basketballs as volleyballs in the basket now, how many balls are there in all?

4 Use Model Approach And Guess And Check Strategy

The 'Guess and Check' strategy can sometimes be used to solve mathematical problems when you do not have a ready method to solve them. As explained in Part A earlier, you need to make intelligent guesses and then check if your guess is correct given the constraints.

The following example shows how you can use the model approach and this strategy to solve some examination questions.

Example 1

Andrew, Jeff and Chris share some marbles. Andrew's share of the marbles is $\frac{1}{4}$ of what Jeff and Chris have together. Jeff's share is $\frac{1}{5}$ of the total number of marbles. If Chris receives 24 more marbles than Jeff,

(a) what fraction of the total number of marbles has Andrew?

(b) find the total number of marbles.

Solution

This is a problem on fractions. However, you will not be able to solve it using the traditional method. In a traditional problem, the total number of marbles is usually given and you can therefore work out Jeff's share of the marbles. In this example, the total number of marbles is not given. Instead, you are asked to find the total number of marbles.

This problem may be solved using the algebraic method. However, pupils in primary schools have not been taught to solve simultaneous equations. Therefore, they have to use the model approach and 'Guess and Check' strategy to solve it.

When you use the 'Guess and Check' strategy, you need to be able to determine what to guess and check. In this question, there are two fractions, $\frac{1}{4}$ and $\frac{1}{5}$. You can start off by drawing a model which shows 20 units so that you can represent the fractions on the bar easily as shown below.

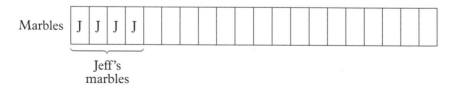

Notice from the model that 4 units are used to represent Jeff's share of the marbles. This is because $\left(\frac{1}{5} \times 20\right)$ equals 4 units.

Next, you have to determine the number of units needed to represent Andrew's and Chris' marbles. In this case, you can use the guess and check strategy. The two conditions that need to be satisfied are as follows:

(1) Chris has more marbles than Andrew.

(2) Andrew has $\frac{1}{4}$ as many marbles as Jeff and Chris have together.

You can then proceed to make your guesses.

1st Guess

Jeff's share is represented by 4 units, Chris' share by 10 units and Andrew's share by 6 units.

Marbles	J	J	J	J	C	C	C	C	C	C	C	C	C	C	A	A	A	A	A	A

               Jeff's   Chris' marbles   Andrew's
              marbles   marbles

Check your guess

Jeff's and Chris' share of the marbles is represented by 14 units.

However, $\left(\frac{1}{4} \times 14\right)$ units is not equal to 6 units. The second condition is not satisfied. Therefore, the guess is wrong.

2nd **Guess**

Jeff's share is re...
Andrew's share by by 4 units, Chris' share by 12 ... and

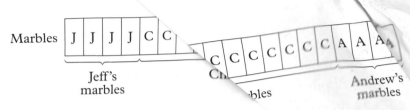

Marbles | J | J | J | J | C | C | C | C | C | C | C | C | A | A | A

Jeff's
marbles

Ch... ...bles

Andrew's
marbles

Check your guess

Jeff's and Chris' share of the marbles is represented by 6 units.

Andrew's share is represented by $\left(\dfrac{1}{4} \times 16\right)$ units or 4 units. The second

condition is satisfied and your guess is correct.

Given that Chris receives 24 more marbles than Jeff, you can work out
the number of marbles represented by 1 unit and hence solve the
problem as follows:

$$12 - 4 = 8$$

$$8 \text{ units} \longrightarrow 24 \text{ marbles}$$

$$1 \text{ unit} \longrightarrow \frac{24}{8} \text{ or } 3 \text{ marbles}$$

$$4 \text{ units} \longrightarrow 12 \text{ marbles}$$

$$12 \text{ units} \longrightarrow (12 \times 3) \text{ or } 36 \text{ marbles}$$

$$20 \text{ units} \longrightarrow 60 \text{ marbles}$$

(a) $\dfrac{4}{20} = \dfrac{1}{5}$

Andrew has $\dfrac{1}{5}$ of the total number of marbles.

(b) The total number of marbles is represented by 20 units. Therefore,
there are 60 marbles altogether.

The follo... xample can be solved by eith... ...ess and Check'
strategy ... model approach.

Example 2

Mrs Che... made some cakes for h... ...ven 3 cakes to each pupil ...s. She gave 5 cakes to each
pupil a... had 4 cakes left. If sh...
instead she would have 64 ca...hen?

(a) H...w many pupils had ...ake?
(b) ...ow many cakes did

Solution (1)

Guess and Ch...ck strategy

You have t... guess the number of pupils Mrs Chen had. Notice that you
are not given the constraints (or conditions) directly in this case. After
studying the question carefully, you will know there are two ways that
Mrs Chen can distribute her cakes. In both cases, the total number of
cakes is the same. You can use this as the constraint to check if your
guessed answer is correct.

1st Guess   40 pupils

1st Case: Total number of cakes = $(40 \times 5) + 4 = 204$

2nd Case: Total number of cakes = $(40 \times 3) + 64 = 184$

In both cases, the total number of cakes is not the same. Therefore, the
guess is wrong.

2nd Guess   30 pupils

1st Case: Total number of cakes = $(30 \times 5) + 4 = 154$

2nd Case: Total number of cakes = $(30 \times 3) + 64 = 154$

In both cases, the total number of cakes is the same. Therefore, the
guess is correct.

(a) Mrs Chen had 30 pupils.
(b) She made 154 cakes.

Note: Your children may find it difficult and tedious to use this strategy
if they are not able to make good guesses. They can use the
model approach to solve it.

Solution (2)

The Model Approach

First of all, draw a bar to represent the number of cakes Mrs Chen made. Next, draw another bar to represent the situation where she had given 5 cakes to each pupil and had 4 cakes left. Finally, draw a bar to represent the situation where she had given 3 cakes to each pupil and had 64 cakes left.

From the model, you will notice the following:

(1) The difference between the number of cakes given to each pupil in the first and second situations is (5 − 3) cakes or 2 cakes.

(2) There is a difference in the length of the second and third bars. This difference represents the difference in the total number of cakes given out in each case.

The difference between the number of cakes that remain in both situations is given by (64 − 4) cakes or 60 cakes. If each pupil received 5 cakes instead of 3 cakes each, how many pupils would have been given the 60 cakes altogether? To work out the answer, you can equate the difference to a simple multiplication statement as follows:

$$\text{Number of pupils} \times 2 \text{ cakes} = \text{Number of cakes needed to top up to}$$
$$5 \text{ cakes from } 3 \text{ cakes for each pupil}$$
$$= 64 - 4 = 60$$

$$\text{Number of pupils} = \frac{60}{2} = 30$$

(a) Therefore, Mrs Chen had 30 pupils.

(b) $(30 \times 5) + 4 = 154$
 She made 154 cakes.

summary, the concept of multiplication is applied to find the number f pupils besides computation skills in subtraction and division. Pupils may have difficulty trying to relate the two 'differences' in the problem. This is why it is important to teach your children to use the model approach so that they can understand the concepts better using concrete representation.

Let's Apply

1. A, B and C are three schools in Singapore. School A has $\frac{1}{4}$ of the total population of the three schools. School A and School B together have three times as many pupils as School C. If School B has 186 pupils more than School A, find the total population of the three schools.

2. X, Y and Z spent a sum of money. X spent $\frac{1}{7}$ of the total amount of money. Z spent one share more than X's and Y's shares combined. If Z spent $75 more than X, find the total amount of money they spent altogether.

3. Mr Lee bought 50 fruits and had $12 left. If he had bought 60 fruits, he would have $8 left.
   (a) What is the cost of one fruit?
   (b) How much money did Mr Lee have at first?

4. Mrs Wong gave 8 sweets to each pupil and had 4 sweets left. If she had given 10 sweets to each pupil, she would need another 16 sweets.
   (a) How many pupils were there?
   (b) How many sweets had Mrs Wong at first?

5 Use Model Approach And Replacement Concept

There are mathematical problems that can be solved using the model approach and the concept of replacement (or substitution). First of all, before you can apply this concept, you need to consider different divisions in terms of parts and units. Next, you have to equate the number of parts for one item with a certain number of units for another item. Then you can replace the number of parts by the number of units or vice versa. This replacement of some parts of one item with some units of another item is done to facilitate computation and hence solve the problem.

The following example on page 92 shows how the model approach and the replacement concept can be applied to solve a certain type of examination questions.

Example

Mrs Leong and Mrs Tan have an equal mass of salt each. Mrs Leong packs her salt into 4 equal packets. Mrs Tan packs her salt into 10 equal packets. Mrs Rajan buys 2 packets of salt from Mrs Leong and 6 packets of salt from Mrs Tan. If Mrs Rajan buys 22 kg of salt in all, what is the total mass of salt Mrs Leong and Mrs Tan have at first?

Solution

First of all, you can draw a model based on the statements in the question. In this problem, each woman has an equal mass of salt. Therefore, the two bars that represent the mass of salt each has must be of the same length as shown below.

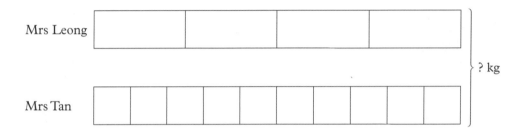

You can divide the bar that represents Mrs Leong's mass of salt into 4 equal divisions (or parts) to show 4 equal packets of salt. Similarly, you can divide the bar that represents Mrs Tan's mass of salt into 10 equal divisions (or units) to show 10 equal packets of salt.

From the model, you will notice that 4 parts of Mrs Leong's salt has the same mass as 10 units of Mrs Tan's salt. You can therefore equate the two representations using simple algebra as follows:

$$4L = 10T$$

Simplifying, $2L = 5T$

From the statements in the question, you know that 2 packets of Mrs Leong's salt and 6 packets of Mrs Tan's salt have a total mass of 22 kg. Therefore, to solve the problem, you can replace 2 packets of Mrs Leong's salt with 5 packets of Mrs Tan's salt and work out the total mass of salt both have as follows:

$$2L + 6T \longrightarrow 22 \text{ kg}$$
$$5T + 6T \longrightarrow 22 \text{ kg}$$
$$11T \longrightarrow 22 \text{ kg}$$
$$1T \longrightarrow 2 \text{ kg}$$
$$10T \longrightarrow 20 \text{ kg}$$
$$20T \longrightarrow 40 \text{ kg}$$

Since Mrs Leong and Mrs Tan have an equal mass of salt, the total mass of salt both women have at first is 40 kg.

From the example, it is obvious that using models can help your child to understand the replacement or substitution concept in algebra better.

Let's Apply

1. Mrs Wu put some cakes into two types of containers: A and B. She put half of the number of cakes equally into 4 identical containers A. She put the rest of the cakes equally into 3 identical containers B. If there were 50 cakes in 6 identical containers A and 3 identical containers B altogether, find the number of cakes Mrs Wu had at first.

2. May and June shared a sack of rice equally. May packed her share of the rice into 3 equal packets. June packed her share into 4 equal packets. If the total mass of 2 packets of May's rice and 8 packets of June's rice is 72 kg, what was the mass of the sack of rice they had originally?

6 Use Make A List Strategy

Drawing a table and making a list of data is one of the strategies you can use to solve some mathematical problems. It can be an alternative approach to solving some problems that require the application of difficult concepts in the solutions. For example, children may come across a problem that requires them to use the concept of division with remainder. They may not have mastered the concept of division and hence will not be able to solve the problem using this concept. However, they can make a list of data to figure out the solution.

The following example shows how you can apply the 'make a list' strategy to solve a problem.

Example

Mr Black earns $2 for each box of fruits sold. He also gets a commission of $5 from his distributor for every 15 boxes of fruits sold. How many boxes of fruits does he sell if he earns

(a) $140?

(b) $191?

Solution

You should notice that this is a very practical problem. The amount of money Mr Black earns depends on the number of boxes of fruits sold. In addition, he is paid a commission of $5 for every 15 boxes of fruits sold.

Firstly, you can compute the amount of money Mr Black earns for each lot of 15 boxes of fruits sold as follows:

Amount of money earned for 1 lot of 15 boxes of fruits
$$= (15 \times \$2) + \$5$$
$$= \$35$$

Secondly, you have to find the number of boxes of fruits he has to sell in order to earn $140. You can start off by finding how many lots of 15 boxes of fruits he needs to sell to earn $140. You can make a list to show the multiples of $35 and multiples of 15 boxes as follows:

Number of boxes of fruits sold	Amount of money earned
15	$35
30	$70
45	$105
60	$140

Notice that $140 is a multiple of $35. You can obtain $140 by multiplying $35 by 4. Similarly, you get 60 boxes by multiplying 15 boxes by 4.

(a) He sells 60 boxes of fruits if he earns $140.

The next part of the question is more difficult because $191 is not a multiple of $35. You can make a list to help you solve the problem.

Number of boxes of fruits sold	Amount of money earned
15	$35
30	$70
45	$105
60	$140
75	$175
90	$210

Notice from the list that $191 lies between $175 and $210. Thus, you can infer that the number of boxes of fruits sold must be between 75 and 90 boxes. Since he earns $191 which is $16 more than $175, you can work out the total number of boxes of fruits sold as follows:

$$\text{Total number of boxes of fruits sold} = 75 + \frac{\$16}{\$2}$$
$$= 75 + 8$$
$$= 83$$

(b) He sells 83 boxes of fruits if he earns $191.

Let's Apply

1. Mrs Lee earns $3 for each T-shirt sold. She earns an additional $10 for every 20 T-shirts sold. How many T-shirts must she sell in order to earn
   (a) $350?
   (b) $368?

2. Mr Chen earns $4 for each pair of shoes sold. If he sells 35 pairs of shoes, he will earn an extra $25. How many pairs of shoes should he sell in order to earn
   (a) $660?
   (b) $740?

Answers

Part A: The Heuristic Approach

1 Guess And Check

1. 8 cars, 6 motorcycles
2. 7 parrots, 11 hamsters
3. 5 postcards, 7 letters
4. Peter wins 6 rounds of the game.
    John wins 10 rounds of the game.

2 Use Pattern

1. 204 squares
2. 650 squares
3. **(a)** 27   **(b)** 72
4. **(a)** 8   **(b)** 40

3 Use Lateral Thinking

1. 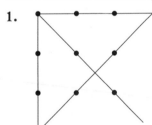   2.

3. Draw a 3-D model of a triangular prism.

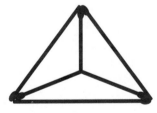

4. Order of girls: Brenda, Amy and Carol. Carol is facing the opposite direction of Brenda and Amy.

4 Use Deductive Thinking

1.

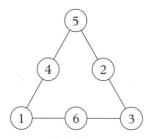

2.

```
      3 8
  +   6 2
  ─────────
    1 0 0
```

3. 18, 0

4.

4	3	8
9	5	1
2	7	6

5 Use Modelling Approach

1. (a) (i)   (ii)   (iii)

(b)

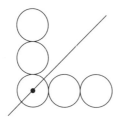

2. (a) Mathematical model: $2 \times 3 - 5$
   (b) Mathematical model: $2 \times 3 = 6$
   (c) Mathematical model: From (a) and (b), $1 + 6 = 7$

3. Make orange juice from the oranges. Then fill the orange juice into two tumblers and pour the orange juice from one tumbler into the other till both tumblers have the same amount of orange juice.

4. Pour the wine into two tumblers until both tumblers have the same amount of wine.

6 Use Investigation

1. Hypothesis: n^2, $50^2 = 2500$
2. Hypothesis: $n^2 = 10\ 000$
3. Hypothesis: $n(n + 1) = 10\ 100$
4. Hypothesis: $\dfrac{n(n - 3)}{2}$, $\dfrac{99(99 - 3)}{2} = 4752$

7 Use Set Concept

1.

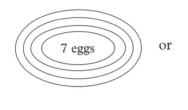 or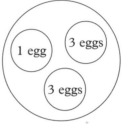

2.

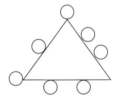

3. 500 g
4. 400 g

Part B: The Model Approach

1 Equal Concept

1. 7
2. 8
3. 8
4. 11

2 **Comparison Concept**
1. 23
2. 15
3. 13
4. 5
5. 26
6. 8

3 **Difference Concept**
1. 70 cents
2. $15
3. $3
4. $16

4 **Multiple Concept**
1. 90 oranges
2. 120 marbles

5 **Difference Concept And Multiple Concept**
1. Joseph sold 30 oranges.
   Larry sold 15 oranges.
   Peter sold 40 oranges.
2. Tina has 48 marbles.
   Sally has 16 marbles.
   Tom has 56 marbles.

6 **Making-A-Whole Concept**
1. Ronnie sold 334 chocolates.
   Ben sold 167 chocolates.
   Ken sold 127 chocolates.
2. Allen has 108 marbles.
   George has 54 marbles.
   Dawn has 80 marbles.

7 **Sharing Concept**
1. (a) 113 oranges (b) 41 oranges
2. (a) 131 cards (b) 33 cards
3. (a) Box A had 125 oranges. (b) 29 oranges
   Box B had 101 oranges.
4. (a) Meimei had 136 cards. (b) 38 cards
   Huihui had 126 cards.

8 Parts-And-Units Concept

1. 40 marbles
2. 20 patients
3. Each doughnut costs 40 cents.
   Each cake costs $2.
4. The mass of each cup is 120 g.
   The mass of each mug is 150 g.

9 Comparing Fractions Concept

1. Bakar had 16 stamps.
   Abu had 4 stamps.
2. Jamie earns $210.
   Shanti earns $630.

Part C: Challenging Examination Problems

1 Use Model Approach And Make Inferences

1. 168 beads
2. $27

2 Use Model Approach And Part-Whole Concept

1. (a) 30 cakes   (b) 2 boxes
2. (a) 96 pears   (b) 5 bags

3 Use Model Approach And Changing Ratio Concept

1. 204 marbles
2. 10.6 litres
3. (a) 40 cows   (b) 140 cows and goats
4. 72 balls

4 Use Model Approach And Guess And Check Strategy

1. 744 pupils
2. $175
3. **(a)** 40 cents   **(b)** $32
4. **(a)** 10 pupils   **(b)** 84 sweets

5 Use Model Approach And Replacement Concept

1. 40 cakes
2. 54 kg

6 Use Make A List Strategy

1. **(a)** 100 T-shirts   **(b)** 106 T-shirts
2. **(a)** 140 pairs of shoes   **(b)** 160 pairs of shoes